DIVINE
SELF-CARE

for Christian Black Women

A DAILY PRAYER JOURNAL FOR SPIRITUAL HEALING WITH BIBLE VERSES, PROMPTS, & ACTIVITIES

DIVINE
SELF-CARE
for Christian Black Women

Intro + How to Use

*A*ll good things come from God. The significance of this is something that many of us know and feel deep in our bones. Today's society is plagued by a number of ills, ranging from absent father households, higher costs of living, widespread mental health issues, and more. As one of the most vulnerable members of society, all of these ailments tend to disproportionately harm Black women. Turning to Christ is the solution needed to combat the afflictions we face.

In the coming pages are five warm-up activities followed by 90+ pages of daily journaling, mood-tracking, gratitude, prayer, and more. This journal will provide you with three months' worth of tracking your spiritual growth and self-care. Each page features a new Bible verse. In all, this book features at least one verse from all 66 books of the Bible.

The Bible, in all its truth and glory, is the perfect answer to many of the challenges that we face as Black women. We can often find ourselves subjected to an onslaught of negativity. The source of this ranges from society, from other races, from our own men, or even from each other. Thus, uplifting and maintaining a positive image of Black women in our hearts and minds is important. Use the daily section "Black women are" to write out a positive affirmation about your fellow sisters. Use this prompt to honor them as someone created in the image of the divine, as we all are (Genesis 1:27).

Again, all good things come from God, including your worth, your femininity, your creativity, your softness as a woman, and happiness itself. Remember this as you sift through this book's pages. With Christ as your guide, may this journal be a source of comfort, inspiration, and growth for all who use it. Here's to starting your self-care journey in the name of The Lord Our God!

Activity 1

FEATURES THE LORD HAS GIVEN ME

AKA: WHAT MAKES ME BEAUTIFUL AS A BLACK WOMAN

NAME:	HEIGHT:
NATIONALITY:	NOSE SHAPE:
HAIR COLOR:	HAIR TEXTURE:
EYE COLOR:	EYE SHAPE:

PERSONALITY TRAITS:

MORAL TRAITS:

I thank God for my ....

Activity 2

CHRIST IS

I AM

Activity 3

WHAT IS
GOD?

WHAT IS
HOLY?

....
....

....
....

....
....

ORDER   *GOODNESS*

MYSELF   *SELF-CARE*

NUTURING   *SOFT*

SLEEP   *SELF-RESPECT*

....
....

....
....

....
....

WHAT IS
FEMININITY?

WHAT IS
SELF-CARE?

What is God?

_____
_____
_____
_____
_____
_____

What is holy?

_____
_____
_____
_____
_____
_____

What is femininity?

_____
_____
_____
_____
_____

What is self-care?

_____
_____
_____
_____
_____

Activity 4

How did God guide me through self-care as a child? (Provide an example.)

_____
_____
_____
_____
_____
_____

How does God guide me through self-care now? (Provide an example.)

_____
_____
_____
_____
_____
_____
_____

What does God feel about all of His people? Give one Bible verse in support.

_____
_____
_____
_____

What does God feel about me as an individual? As a Black woman?

_____
_____
_____
_____
_____

ELABORATE

(OPTIONAL)

Activity 5

SELECT ALL THAT APPLY:

☐ SKINCARE   ☐ EATING HABITS   ☐ BEING MORE ACTIVE

☐ SLEEP HYGIENE   ☐ MENTAL HEALTH   ☐ HOME CLEANING

☐ IMPROVED RELATIONSHIPS   ☐ SPIRITUAL GROWTH   ☐ ....

....

CONCERNS & CHALLENGES

_____

_____

_____

_____

_____

_____

_____

_____

_____

_____

_____

_____

_____

_____

ELABORATE

PRAYER: Lord, I know in you I can become anew (2 Corinthians 5:17). I ask you to help me find the way.

SKINCARE:

I pray for

_____

_____

_____

EATING HABITS:

I pray for

_____

_____

_____

BEING MORE ACTIVE:

I pray for

_____

_____

_____

SLEEP HYGIENE:

I pray for

_____

_____

_____

MENTAL HEALTH:

I pray for

_____

_____

_____

HOME CLEANING:

I pray for

_____

_____

_____

RELATIONSHIPS:

I pray for

_____

_____

_____

SPIRITUAL GROWTH:

I pray for

_____

_____

_____

.... : I pray for

_____

- - - (OUT OF 10)

HOURS SLEPT	ENERGY
4.5	5

MOOD

TODAY'S GOALS: Clean bedroom, hair wash day, go to bed earlier

BLACK WOMEN ARE the fastest-growing entrepeneurs, the most enrolled in college

I THANK GOD FOR...

1. my job
2. my good health
3. the beautiful weather today

VERSE OF THE DAY	PSALMS 34:4

I sought Yahweh, and he answered me, and delivered me from all my fears.

I PRAY FOR my family, war-torn countries, and a productive day

FOOD INTAKE

- Ham and cheese omlette
- Chicken soup
- 2 large doughnuts
- Steak + coleslaw
- Berries and cream

ACTIVITIES

- Walked to church
- Walked dog for 30 min.
- Jumped rope 15 min.

☐ **MORNING SKINCARE**

☑ take supplements

☐ _____

☑ **EVENING SKINCARE**

JOURNAL ENTRY

I feel a little out of it today. I went to bed too late. I'll try to do better. I'm happy I saw my friend today, it's been so long. I thought maybe we weren't friends anymore, but the Lord has brought us together again. Also, I'll see if the doughnuts I ate are going to break me out. I'll look up a healthier alternative for my doughnut cravings.

DATE _____ M T W T F S S

HOURS SLEPT	ENERGY

MOOD

VERSE OF THE DAY | GALATIANS 1:10

TODAY'S GOALS: _____

_____

I PRAY FOR

BLACK WOMEN ARE

FOOD INTAKE

I THANK GOD FOR...

1. _____
2. _____
3. _____

ACTIVITIES

JOURNAL ENTRY

☐ **MORNING SKINCARE**

☐ _____

☐ _____

☐ **EVENING SKINCARE**

DATE _____ M T W T F S S

HOURS SLEPT	ENERGY

MOOD
😠 😟 😐 🙂 😄

VERSE OF THE DAY | **PROVERBS 10:4**
_____
_____
_____

TODAY'S GOALS: _____
_____

I PRAY FOR

BLACK WOMEN ARE

FOOD INTAKE

I THANK GOD FOR...

1. _____
2. _____
3. _____

ACTIVITIES

☐ **MORNING SKINCARE**

☐ _____

☐ _____

☐ **EVENING SKINCARE**

JOURNAL ENTRY
_____
_____
_____
_____
_____
_____
_____
_____
_____
_____
_____
_____

DATE _____ M T W T F S S

HOURS SLEPT	ENERGY

MOOD

☹ ☹ 😐 🙂 😄

TODAY'S GOALS: _____

_____

BLACK WOMEN ARE

I THANK GOD FOR...

1. _____
2. _____
3. _____

VERSE OF THE DAY	JUDE 1:24

_____
_____
_____
_____

I PRAY FOR

FOOD INTAKE

ACTIVITIES

☐ **MORNING SKINCARE**

☐ _____

☐ _____

☐ **EVENING SKINCARE**

JOURNAL ENTRY

_____
_____
_____
_____
_____
_____
_____
_____
_____
_____
_____
_____
_____

DATE _____ M T W T F S S

HOURS SLEPT	ENERGY

MOOD

VERSE OF THE DAY | **ROMANS 8:28**

TODAY'S GOALS: _____

I PRAY FOR

BLACK WOMEN ARE

FOOD INTAKE

I THANK GOD FOR...

1. _____
2. _____
3. _____

ACTIVITIES

JOURNAL ENTRY

☐ **MORNING SKINCARE**

☐ _____

☐ _____

☐ **EVENING SKINCARE**

DATE _____ M T W T F S S

HOURS SLEPT	ENERGY

MOOD

TODAY'S GOALS: _____

_____

BLACK WOMEN ARE

I THANK GOD FOR...

1. _____
2. _____
3. _____

_____

_____

_____

_____

I PRAY FOR

FOOD INTAKE

ACTIVITIES

☐ **MORNING SKINCARE**

☐ _____

☐ _____

☐ **EVENING SKINCARE**

JOURNAL ENTRY

_____

_____

_____

_____

_____

_____

_____

_____

_____

_____

_____

_____

_____

DATE _____ M T W T F S S

HOURS SLEPT	ENERGY

MOOD

😠 ☹️ 😐 🙂 😄

TODAY'S GOALS: _____

_____

BLACK WOMEN ARE

I THANK GOD FOR...

1. _____
2. _____
3. _____

VERSE OF THE DAY | OBADIAH 1:15

_____

_____

_____

I PRAY FOR

FOOD INTAKE

ACTIVITIES

☐ **MORNING SKINCARE**

☐ _____

☐ _____

☐ **EVENING SKINCARE**

JOURNAL ENTRY

_____
_____
_____
_____
_____
_____
_____
_____
_____
_____
_____
_____
_____
_____

DATE _____ **M T W T F S S**

HOURS SLEPT	ENERGY

MOOD

VERSE OF THE DAY | **PROVERBS 18:24**

TODAY'S GOALS: _____

_____

I PRAY FOR

BLACK WOMEN ARE

FOOD INTAKE

I THANK GOD FOR...

1. _____
2. _____
3. _____

ACTIVITIES

JOURNAL ENTRY

☐ **MORNING SKINCARE**

☐ _____

☐ _____

☐ **EVENING SKINCARE**

DATE _____ M T W T F S S

HOURS SLEPT	ENERGY

MOOD

😠 ☹️ 😐 🙂 😄

TODAY'S GOALS: _____

_____

BLACK WOMEN ARE

I THANK GOD FOR...

1. _____
2. _____
3. _____

VERSE OF THE DAY	GENESIS 3:13

I PRAY FOR

FOOD INTAKE

ACTIVITIES

JOURNAL ENTRY

☐ **MORNING SKINCARE**

☐ _____

☐ _____

☐ **EVENING SKINCARE**

DATE _____ M T W T F S S

HOURS SLEPT	ENERGY

VERSE OF THE DAY | **ZEPHANIAH 3:17**

MOOD

☹ ☹ ☺ ☺ 😄

TODAY'S GOALS: _____

_____

I PRAY FOR

BLACK WOMEN ARE

FOOD INTAKE

I THANK GOD FOR...

1. _____
2. _____
3. _____

ACTIVITIES

JOURNAL ENTRY

☐ **MORNING SKINCARE**

☐ _____

☐ _____

☐ **EVENING SKINCARE**

DATE _____ M T W T F S S

HOURS SLEPT	ENERGY

VERSE OF THE DAY	LEVITICUS 19:18

MOOD

😠 🙁 😐 🙂 😄

TODAY'S GOALS: _____
_____

I PRAY FOR

BLACK WOMEN ARE

FOOD INTAKE

I THANK GOD FOR...

1. _____
2. _____
3. _____

ACTIVITIES

☐ **MORNING SKINCARE**

☐ _____

☐ _____

☐ **EVENING SKINCARE**

JOURNAL ENTRY

DATE _____ M T W T F S S

HOURS SLEPT	ENERGY

MOOD

VERSE OF THE DAY	MATTHEW 10:34

_____
_____
_____
_____

TODAY'S GOALS: _____

_____

I PRAY FOR
_____
_____

BLACK WOMEN ARE

FOOD INTAKE

I THANK GOD FOR...

1. _____
2. _____
3. _____

ACTIVITIES

JOURNAL ENTRY

☐ **MORNING SKINCARE**

☐ _____

☐ _____

☐ **EVENING SKINCARE**

DATE _____ M T W T F S S

HOURS SLEPT	ENERGY

MOOD

_____

_____

_____

_____

TODAY'S GOALS: _____

_____

I PRAY FOR
_____
_____
_____

BLACK WOMEN ARE
_____

FOOD INTAKE

I THANK GOD FOR...

1. _____

2. _____

3. _____

ACTIVITIES

JOURNAL ENTRY

☐ MORNING SKINCARE

☐ _____

☐ _____

☐ EVENING SKINCARE

DATE _____ M T W T F S S

HOURS SLEPT	ENERGY

MOOD

☹ ☹ 😐 🙂 😄

TODAY'S GOALS: _____

_____

BLACK WOMEN ARE

I THANK GOD FOR...

1. _____
2. _____
3. _____

VERSE OF THE DAY — LAMENTA. 3:22-23

_____
_____
_____
_____

I PRAY FOR

FOOD INTAKE

ACTIVITIES

JOURNAL ENTRY

☐ MORNING SKINCARE

☐ _____

☐ _____

☐ EVENING SKINCARE

DATE _____ M T W T F S S

HOURS SLEPT	ENERGY

MOOD

😠 ☹️ 😐 🙂 😄

VERSE OF THE DAY | **2 JOHN 1:6**
_____
_____
_____
_____

TODAY'S GOALS: _____
_____

I PRAY FOR
_____
_____

BLACK WOMEN ARE

I THANK GOD FOR...

1. _____
2. _____
3. _____

FOOD INTAKE

ACTIVITIES

JOURNAL ENTRY

_____
_____
_____
_____
_____
_____
_____

☐ **MORNING SKINCARE**

☐ _____

☐ _____

☐ **EVENING SKINCARE**

DATE _____ M T W T F S S

HOURS SLEPT	ENERGY

VERSE OF THE DAY	1 THESSA. 5:16-18

_____
_____
_____
_____

MOOD

😠 ☹️ 😐 🙂 😄

TODAY'S GOALS: _____

_____

I PRAY FOR

BLACK WOMEN ARE

FOOD INTAKE

I THANK GOD FOR...

1. _____
2. _____
3. _____

ACTIVITIES

JOURNAL ENTRY

_____
_____
_____
_____
_____

☐ **MORNING SKINCARE**

☐ _____

☐ _____

☐ **EVENING SKINCARE**

_____
_____
_____
_____

DATE _____ M T W T F S S

HOURS SLEPT	ENERGY

MOOD

😠 ☹️ 😐 🙂 😄

VERSE OF THE DAY | **EXODUS 20:3**

_____
_____
_____
_____

TODAY'S GOALS: _____

_____

I PRAY FOR
_____
_____

BLACK WOMEN ARE

I THANK GOD FOR...

1. _____
2. _____
3. _____

FOOD INTAKE

ACTIVITIES

☐ **MORNING SKINCARE**

☐ _____

☐ _____

☐ **EVENING SKINCARE**

JOURNAL ENTRY

_____
_____
_____
_____
_____
_____
_____
_____
_____
_____
_____
_____

DATE _____ M T W T F S S

HOURS SLEPT	ENERGY

VERSE OF THE DAY | **NAHUM 1:7**

_____
_____
_____
_____

MOOD

☹ 🙁 😐 🙂 😁

TODAY'S GOALS: _____

_____

I PRAY FOR

_____
_____

BLACK WOMEN ARE

FOOD INTAKE

I THANK GOD FOR...

1. _____
2. _____
3. _____

ACTIVITIES

JOURNAL ENTRY

☐ **MORNING SKINCARE**

☐ _____

☐ _____

☐ **EVENING SKINCARE**

DATE _____ M T W T F S S

HOURS SLEPT	ENERGY

VERSE OF THE DAY	PSALMS 19:1

MOOD

😠 ☹️ 😐 🙂 😄

I PRAY FOR

TODAY'S GOALS: _____

_____

BLACK WOMEN ARE

FOOD INTAKE

I THANK GOD FOR...

1. _____
2. _____
3. _____

ACTIVITIES

JOURNAL ENTRY

☐ **MORNING SKINCARE**

☐ _____

☐ _____

☐ **EVENING SKINCARE**

DATE _____ M T W T F S S

HOURS SLEPT	ENERGY

MOOD

VERSE OF THE DAY | REVELATION 21:4

I PRAY FOR

TODAY'S GOALS: _____

_____

BLACK WOMEN ARE

FOOD INTAKE

I THANK GOD FOR...

1. _____
2. _____
3. _____

ACTIVITIES

JOURNAL ENTRY

☐ **MORNING SKINCARE**

☐ _____

☐ _____

☐ **EVENING SKINCARE**

DATE _____ M T W T F S S

HOURS SLEPT	ENERGY

MOOD

TODAY'S GOALS: _____

_____

BLACK WOMEN ARE

I THANK GOD FOR...

1. _____
2. _____
3. _____

VERSE OF THE DAY | DANIEL 2:20-22

_____

_____

_____

_____

I PRAY FOR

FOOD INTAKE

ACTIVITIES

☐ **MORNING SKINCARE**

☐ _____

☐ _____

☐ **EVENING SKINCARE**

JOURNAL ENTRY

DATE _____ M T W T F S S

HOURS SLEPT	ENERGY

VERSE OF THE DAY	TITUS 2:5

MOOD

☹ 🙁 😐 🙂 😄

I PRAY FOR

TODAY'S GOALS: _____

_____

BLACK WOMEN ARE

FOOD INTAKE

I THANK GOD FOR...

1. _____
2. _____
3. _____

ACTIVITIES

JOURNAL ENTRY

☐ **MORNING SKINCARE**

☐ _____

☐ _____

☐ **EVENING SKINCARE**

DATE _____ M T W T F S S

HOURS SLEPT	ENERGY

VERSE OF THE DAY | **DEUTERO. 31:6**

MOOD

TODAY'S GOALS: _____

_____

I PRAY FOR

BLACK WOMEN ARE

FOOD INTAKE

I THANK GOD FOR...

1. _____
2. _____
3. _____

ACTIVITIES

JOURNAL ENTRY

☐ **MORNING SKINCARE**

☐ _____

☐ _____

☐ **EVENING SKINCARE**

DATE _____ M T W T F S S

HOURS SLEPT	ENERGY

VERSE OF THE DAY	1 CORINTHI. 13:4

MOOD

I PRAY FOR

TODAY'S GOALS: _____

_____

BLACK WOMEN ARE

FOOD INTAKE

I THANK GOD FOR...

1. _____
2. _____
3. _____

ACTIVITIES

JOURNAL ENTRY

☐ **MORNING SKINCARE**

☐ _____

☐ _____

☐ **EVENING SKINCARE**

DATE _____ M T W T F S S

HOURS SLEPT	ENERGY

VERSE OF THE DAY	JUDGES 5:3

_____

_____

_____

MOOD

I PRAY FOR

TODAY'S GOALS: _____

_____

BLACK WOMEN ARE

FOOD INTAKE

I THANK GOD FOR...

1. _____
2. _____
3. _____

ACTIVITIES

JOURNAL ENTRY

☐ MORNING SKINCARE

☐ _____

☐ _____

☐ EVENING SKINCARE

DATE _____ M T W T F S S

HOURS SLEPT	ENERGY

VERSE OF THE DAY	SONG OF SOL. 8:7

_____

_____

_____

_____

MOOD

☹ ☹ 😐 🙂 😄

I PRAY FOR

TODAY'S GOALS: _____

_____

BLACK WOMEN ARE

FOOD INTAKE

I THANK GOD FOR...

1. _____
2. _____
3. _____

ACTIVITIES

JOURNAL ENTRY

_____

_____

_____

_____

☐ **MORNING SKINCARE**

☐ _____

☐ _____

☐ **EVENING SKINCARE**

DATE _____ M T W T F S S

HOURS SLEPT	ENERGY

VERSE OF THE DAY | **PROVERBS 28:26**

MOOD

😠 ☹️ 😐 🙂 😄

TODAY'S GOALS: _____

_____

I PRAY FOR

BLACK WOMEN ARE

FOOD INTAKE

I THANK GOD FOR...

1. _____
2. _____
3. _____

ACTIVITIES

JOURNAL ENTRY

☐ **MORNING SKINCARE**

☐ _____

☐ _____

☐ **EVENING SKINCARE**

DATE _____ M T W T F S S

HOURS SLEPT	ENERGY

MOOD

☹ ☹ ☺ ☺ 😄

VERSE OF THE DAY | **1 PETER 5:7**
_____
_____
_____
_____

TODAY'S GOALS: _____
_____

I PRAY FOR
_____
_____

BLACK WOMEN ARE
_____

FOOD INTAKE

I THANK GOD FOR...

1. _____
2. _____
3. _____

ACTIVITIES

JOURNAL ENTRY

☐ MORNING SKINCARE

☐ _____

☐ _____

☐ EVENING SKINCARE

DATE _____ M T W T F S S

HOURS SLEPT	ENERGY

MOOD

TODAY'S GOALS: _____

_____

I PRAY FOR

BLACK WOMEN ARE

FOOD INTAKE

I THANK GOD FOR...

1. _____
2. _____
3. _____

ACTIVITIES

JOURNAL ENTRY

☐ **MORNING SKINCARE**

☐ _____

☐ _____

☐ **EVENING SKINCARE**

DATE _____ M T W T F S S

HOURS SLEPT	ENERGY

VERSE OF THE DAY | **2 SAMUEL 22:31**
_____
_____
_____
_____
_____

MOOD

😠 🙁 😐 🙂 😁

TODAY'S GOALS: _____
_____

I PRAY FOR
_____
_____

BLACK WOMEN ARE
_____

FOOD INTAKE

I THANK GOD FOR...

1. _____
2. _____
3. _____

ACTIVITIES

JOURNAL ENTRY

☐ **MORNING SKINCARE**

☐ _____

☐ _____

☐ **EVENING SKINCARE**

DATE _____ M T W T F S S

HOURS SLEPT	ENERGY

MOOD

😠 ☹️ 😐 🙂 😄

TODAY'S GOALS: _____

_____

BLACK WOMEN ARE

I THANK GOD FOR...

1. _____

2. _____

3. _____

VERSE OF THE DAY	PROVERBS 18:21

_____
_____
_____
_____

I PRAY FOR

FOOD INTAKE

ACTIVITIES

☐ **MORNING SKINCARE**

☐ _____

☐ _____

☐ **EVENING SKINCARE**

JOURNAL ENTRY

_____
_____
_____
_____
_____
_____
_____
_____
_____
_____
_____
_____

DATE _____ M T W T F S S

HOURS SLEPT	ENERGY

MOOD

VERSE OF THE DAY | **MICAH 6:8**

TODAY'S GOALS: _____

_____

I PRAY FOR

BLACK WOMEN ARE

FOOD INTAKE

I THANK GOD FOR...

1. _____
2. _____
3. _____

ACTIVITIES

JOURNAL ENTRY

☐ **MORNING SKINCARE**

☐ _____

☐ _____

☐ **EVENING SKINCARE**

DATE _____ M T W T F S S

HOURS SLEPT	ENERGY

MOOD

VERSE OF THE DAY	PHILEMON 1:4

_____
_____
_____
_____

TODAY'S GOALS: _____
_____

I PRAY FOR

BLACK WOMEN ARE

I THANK GOD FOR...

1. _____
2. _____
3. _____

FOOD INTAKE

ACTIVITIES

☐ **MORNING SKINCARE**

☐ _____

☐ _____

☐ **EVENING SKINCARE**

JOURNAL ENTRY

_____
_____
_____
_____
_____
_____
_____
_____
_____
_____
_____
_____
_____

DATE _____ M T W T F S S

HOURS SLEPT	ENERGY

MOOD

VERSE OF THE DAY | **3 JOHN 1:11**

_____
_____
_____
_____

TODAY'S GOALS: _____

_____

I PRAY FOR

BLACK WOMEN ARE

FOOD INTAKE

I THANK GOD FOR...

1. _____
2. _____
3. _____

ACTIVITIES

JOURNAL ENTRY

☐ **MORNING SKINCARE**

☐ _____

☐ _____

☐ **EVENING SKINCARE**

DATE _____ M T W T F S S

HOURS SLEPT	ENERGY

VERSE OF THE DAY	NEHEMIAH 8:10

_____
_____
_____
_____

MOOD

😠 ☹️ 😐 🙂 😄

I PRAY FOR

TODAY'S GOALS: _____

_____

BLACK WOMEN ARE

FOOD INTAKE

I THANK GOD FOR...

1. _____
2. _____
3. _____

ACTIVITIES

JOURNAL ENTRY

☐ **MORNING SKINCARE**

☐ _____

☐ _____

☐ **EVENING SKINCARE**

DATE _____ M T W T F S S

HOURS SLEPT	ENERGY

MOOD

☹ 🙁 😐 🙂 😄

TODAY'S GOALS: _____

_____

VERSE OF THE DAY	LUKE 6:31

_____
_____
_____
_____

I PRAY FOR

BLACK WOMEN ARE

I THANK GOD FOR...

1. _____
2. _____
3. _____

FOOD INTAKE

ACTIVITIES

JOURNAL ENTRY

☐ **MORNING SKINCARE**

☐ _____

☐ _____

☐ **EVENING SKINCARE**

DATE _____ M T W T F S S

HOURS SLEPT	ENERGY

MOOD

😠 🙁 😐 🙂 😄

VERSE OF THE DAY | **1 SAMUEL 16:7**

TODAY'S GOALS: _____

_____

I PRAY FOR

BLACK WOMEN ARE

FOOD INTAKE

I THANK GOD FOR...

1. _____
2. _____
3. _____

ACTIVITIES

JOURNAL ENTRY

☐ **MORNING SKINCARE**

☐ _____

☐ _____

☐ **EVENING SKINCARE**

DATE _____ M T W T F S S

HOURS SLEPT	ENERGY

VERSE OF THE DAY | **HAGGAI 1:4**

_____
_____
_____
_____

MOOD

☹ 🙁 😐 🙂 😄

TODAY'S GOALS: _____

_____

I PRAY FOR
_____
_____

BLACK WOMEN ARE

FOOD INTAKE

I THANK GOD FOR...

1. _____
2. _____
3. _____

ACTIVITIES

JOURNAL ENTRY

☐ **MORNING SKINCARE**

☐ _____

☐ _____

☐ **EVENING SKINCARE**

DATE _____ M T W T F S S

HOURS SLEPT	ENERGY

MOOD

😠 🙁 😐 🙂 😄

TODAY'S GOALS: _____

_____

VERSE OF THE DAY | PHILIPPIANS 4:13

_____
_____
_____
_____

I PRAY FOR

_____
_____

BLACK WOMEN ARE

_____

I THANK GOD FOR...

1. _____
2. _____
3. _____

FOOD INTAKE

_____
_____
_____
_____
_____
_____
_____

ACTIVITIES

JOURNAL ENTRY

☐ **MORNING SKINCARE**

☐ _____

☐ _____

☐ **EVENING SKINCARE**

DATE _____ M T W T F S S

HOURS SLEPT	ENERGY

MOOD

VERSE OF THE DAY | **PROVERBS 27:20**

_____
_____
_____
_____

TODAY'S GOALS: _____

_____

I PRAY FOR

BLACK WOMEN ARE

FOOD INTAKE

I THANK GOD FOR...

1. _____
2. _____
3. _____

ACTIVITIES

JOURNAL ENTRY

☐ MORNING SKINCARE

☐ _____

☐ _____

☐ EVENING SKINCARE

DATE _____ M T W T F S S

HOURS SLEPT	ENERGY

MOOD

VERSE OF THE DAY | **2 THESSALO. 3:3**

_____
_____
_____
_____

TODAY'S GOALS: _____

_____

I PRAY FOR

BLACK WOMEN ARE

I THANK GOD FOR...

1. _____
2. _____
3. _____

FOOD INTAKE

ACTIVITIES

JOURNAL ENTRY

_____
_____
_____
_____
_____
_____
_____

☐ **MORNING SKINCARE**

☐ _____

☐ _____

☐ **EVENING SKINCARE**

DATE _____ M T W T F S S

HOURS SLEPT	ENERGY

MOOD

😠 🙁 😐 🙂 😄

VERSE OF THE DAY | JOEL 2:25

_____
_____
_____
_____

TODAY'S GOALS: _____

_____

I PRAY FOR

BLACK WOMEN ARE

FOOD INTAKE

I THANK GOD FOR...

1. _____
2. _____
3. _____

ACTIVITIES

☐ **MORNING SKINCARE**

☐ _____

☐ _____

☐ **EVENING SKINCARE**

JOURNAL ENTRY

_____
_____
_____
_____
_____
_____
_____
_____
_____
_____
_____

DATE _____ **M T W T F S S**

HOURS SLEPT	ENERGY

MOOD

☹ ☹ 😐 🙂 😄

TODAY'S GOALS: _____
_____

BLACK WOMEN ARE

I THANK GOD FOR...

1. _____
2. _____
3. _____

VERSE OF THE DAY	1 CHRONI. 16:11

I PRAY FOR

FOOD INTAKE

ACTIVITIES

JOURNAL ENTRY

☐ **MORNING SKINCARE**

☐ _____

☐ _____

☐ **EVENING SKINCARE**

DATE _____ M T W T F S S

HOURS SLEPT	ENERGY

MOOD

😠 🙁 😐 🙂 😄

TODAY'S GOALS: _____

_____

BLACK WOMEN ARE

I THANK GOD FOR...

1. _____

2. _____

3. _____

ACTIVITIES

☐ MORNING SKINCARE

☐ _____

☐ _____

☐ EVENING SKINCARE

VERSE OF THE DAY — JONAH 2:2

_____
_____
_____
_____

I PRAY FOR

FOOD INTAKE

JOURNAL ENTRY

_____
_____
_____
_____
_____
_____
_____
_____
_____
_____
_____
_____
_____

DATE _____ M T W T F S S

HOURS SLEPT	ENERGY

VERSE OF THE DAY	1 TIMOTHY 6:12

MOOD

😠 ☹️ 😐 🙂 😄

TODAY'S GOALS: _____

_____

I PRAY FOR

BLACK WOMEN ARE

FOOD INTAKE

I THANK GOD FOR...

1. _____
2. _____
3. _____

ACTIVITIES

JOURNAL ENTRY

☐ **MORNING SKINCARE**

☐ _____

☐ _____

☐ **EVENING SKINCARE**

DATE _____ M T W T F S S

HOURS SLEPT	ENERGY

MOOD

VERSE OF THE DAY — **ZECHARIAH 4:6**

_____
_____
_____
_____

TODAY'S GOALS: _____

_____

I PRAY FOR

BLACK WOMEN ARE

I THANK GOD FOR...

1. _____
2. _____
3. _____

FOOD INTAKE

ACTIVITIES

☐ **MORNING SKINCARE**

☐ _____

☐ _____

☐ **EVENING SKINCARE**

JOURNAL ENTRY

_____
_____
_____
_____
_____
_____
_____
_____
_____
_____
_____
_____

DATE _____ **M T W T F S S**

HOURS SLEPT	ENERGY

VERSE OF THE DAY	PSALM 23:1

_____
_____
_____
_____

MOOD

TODAY'S GOALS: _____

_____

I PRAY FOR

BLACK WOMEN ARE

I THANK GOD FOR...

1. _____

2. _____

3. _____

FOOD INTAKE

ACTIVITIES

JOURNAL ENTRY

_____
_____
_____
_____
_____
_____

☐ **MORNING SKINCARE**

☐ _____

☐ _____

☐ **EVENING SKINCARE**

_____
_____
_____
_____

DATE _____ M T W T F S S

HOURS SLEPT	ENERGY

VERSE OF THE DAY | **PROVERBS 6:27**

MOOD

☹ 🙁 😐 🙂 😄

TODAY'S GOALS: _____

_____

I PRAY FOR

BLACK WOMEN ARE

FOOD INTAKE

I THANK GOD FOR...

1. _____
2. _____
3. _____

ACTIVITIES

JOURNAL ENTRY

☐ **MORNING SKINCARE**

☐ _____

☐ _____

☐ **EVENING SKINCARE**

DATE _____ M T W T F S S

HOURS SLEPT	ENERGY

MOOD

😠 ☹️ 😐 🙂 😄

| VERSE OF THE DAY | JOHN 3:16 |

TODAY'S GOALS: _____

_____

I PRAY FOR

_____

_____

BLACK WOMEN ARE

FOOD INTAKE

I THANK GOD FOR...

1. _____
2. _____
3. _____

ACTIVITIES

JOURNAL ENTRY

☐ **MORNING SKINCARE**

☐ _____

☐ _____

☐ **EVENING SKINCARE**

DATE _____ M T W T F S S

HOURS SLEPT	ENERGY

VERSE OF THE DAY | JEREMIAH 29:11

_____
_____
_____
_____

MOOD

I PRAY FOR
_____
_____

TODAY'S GOALS: _____

_____

FOOD INTAKE

BLACK WOMEN ARE
_____

I THANK GOD FOR...

1. _____
2. _____
3. _____

ACTIVITIES

JOURNAL ENTRY

☐ MORNING SKINCARE

☐ _____

☐ _____

☐ EVENING SKINCARE

DATE _____ M T W T F S S

HOURS SLEPT	ENERGY

VERSE OF THE DAY	PSALMS 20:4

MOOD

😠 🙁 😐 🙂 😄

TODAY'S GOALS: _____

_____

BLACK WOMEN ARE

I THANK GOD FOR...

1. _____
2. _____
3. _____

I PRAY FOR

FOOD INTAKE

ACTIVITIES

JOURNAL ENTRY

☐ **MORNING SKINCARE**

☐ _____

☐ _____

☐ **EVENING SKINCARE**

DATE _____ M T W T F S S

HOURS SLEPT	ENERGY

MOOD

TODAY'S GOALS: _____

_____

BLACK WOMEN ARE

I THANK GOD FOR...

1. _____
2. _____
3. _____

VERSE OF THE DAY | **MALACHI 3:10**

_____
_____
_____
_____

I PRAY FOR

FOOD INTAKE

ACTIVITIES

☐ **MORNING SKINCARE**

☐ _____

☐ _____

☐ **EVENING SKINCARE**

JOURNAL ENTRY

DATE _____ M T W T F S S

HOURS SLEPT	ENERGY

VERSE OF THE DAY	ACTS 4:12

MOOD

😠 ☹️ 😐 🙂 😄

TODAY'S GOALS: _____

_____

I PRAY FOR

BLACK WOMEN ARE

FOOD INTAKE

I THANK GOD FOR...

1. _____
2. _____
3. _____

ACTIVITIES

JOURNAL ENTRY

☐ **MORNING SKINCARE**

☐ _____

☐ _____

☐ **EVENING SKINCARE**

DATE _____ M T W T F S S

HOURS SLEPT	ENERGY

MOOD

😠 ☹️ 😐 🙂 😄

VERSE OF THE DAY | **PROVERBS 22:7**
_____
_____
_____
_____

TODAY'S GOALS: _____
_____

I PRAY FOR
_____
_____

BLACK WOMEN ARE
_____

FOOD INTAKE

I THANK GOD FOR...

1. _____
2. _____
3. _____

ACTIVITIES

JOURNAL ENTRY

☐ **MORNING SKINCARE**

☐ _____

☐ _____

☐ **EVENING SKINCARE**

DATE _____ M T W T F S S

HOURS SLEPT	ENERGY

VERSE OF THE DAY	2 PETER 1:3

MOOD

😠 ☹️ 😐 🙂 😁

TODAY'S GOALS: _____

_____

I PRAY FOR

BLACK WOMEN ARE

I THANK GOD FOR...

1. _____
2. _____
3. _____

FOOD INTAKE

ACTIVITIES

JOURNAL ENTRY

☐ **MORNING SKINCARE**

☐ _____

☐ _____

☐ **EVENING SKINCARE**

DATE _____ M T W T F S S

HOURS SLEPT	ENERGY

VERSE OF THE DAY	EZEKIEL 36:26

_____
_____
_____
_____

MOOD

😠 ☹️ 😐 🙂 😄

TODAY'S GOALS: _____

_____

I PRAY FOR

BLACK WOMEN ARE

FOOD INTAKE

I THANK GOD FOR...

1. _____
2. _____
3. _____

ACTIVITIES

JOURNAL ENTRY

_____
_____
_____
_____
_____
_____

☐ **MORNING SKINCARE**

☐ _____

☐ _____

_____
_____
_____

☐ **EVENING SKINCARE**

DATE _____ **M T W T F S S**

HOURS SLEPT	ENERGY

MOOD
😠 ☹️ 😐 🙂 😄

TODAY'S GOALS: _____
_____

BLACK WOMEN ARE

I THANK GOD FOR...

1. _____
2. _____
3. _____

VERSE OF THE DAY	NUMBERS 6:24-26

_____
_____
_____
_____

I PRAY FOR

FOOD INTAKE

ACTIVITIES

☐ **MORNING SKINCARE**

☐ _____

☐ _____

☐ **EVENING SKINCARE**

JOURNAL ENTRY

_____
_____
_____
_____
_____
_____
_____
_____
_____
_____
_____
_____

DATE _____ M T W T F S S

HOURS SLEPT	ENERGY

VERSE OF THE DAY	ISAIAH 7:14

_____
_____
_____
_____

MOOD

😠 🙁 😐 🙂 😁

I PRAY FOR

TODAY'S GOALS: _____

_____

BLACK WOMEN ARE

FOOD INTAKE

I THANK GOD FOR...

1. _____
2. _____
3. _____

ACTIVITIES	JOURNAL ENTRY

☐ MORNING SKINCARE

☐ _____

☐ _____

☐ EVENING SKINCARE

DATE _____ **M T W T F S S**

HOURS SLEPT	ENERGY

MOOD

😠 ☹️ 😐 🙂 😄

VERSE OF THE DAY	RUTH 1:16

_____

_____

_____

_____

TODAY'S GOALS: _____

_____

I PRAY FOR
_____
_____

BLACK WOMEN ARE
_____

FOOD INTAKE

I THANK GOD FOR...

1. _____
2. _____
3. _____

ACTIVITIES

JOURNAL ENTRY

☐ **MORNING SKINCARE**

☐ _____

☐ _____

☐ **EVENING SKINCARE**

DATE _____ M T W T F S S

HOURS SLEPT	ENERGY

MOOD

VERSE OF THE DAY | PROVERBS 26:4

_____
_____
_____
_____

I PRAY FOR

TODAY'S GOALS: _____

_____

BLACK WOMEN ARE

FOOD INTAKE

I THANK GOD FOR...

1. _____

2. _____

3. _____

ACTIVITIES

JOURNAL ENTRY

☐ MORNING SKINCARE

☐ _____

☐ _____

☐ EVENING SKINCARE

DATE _____ M T W T F S S

HOURS SLEPT	ENERGY

VERSE OF THE DAY	AMOS 5:24

MOOD

😠 ☹️ 😐 🙂 😄

TODAY'S GOALS: _____

_____

I PRAY FOR

BLACK WOMEN ARE

I THANK GOD FOR...

1. _____
2. _____
3. _____

FOOD INTAKE

ACTIVITIES

JOURNAL ENTRY

☐ **MORNING SKINCARE**

☐ _____

☐ _____

☐ **EVENING SKINCARE**

DATE _____ M T W T F S S

HOURS SLEPT	ENERGY

MOOD
😠 😞 😐 🙂 😄

VERSE OF THE DAY | **COLOSSIANS 3:23**
_____
_____
_____
_____

TODAY'S GOALS: _____
_____

I PRAY FOR
_____
_____

BLACK WOMEN ARE
_____

I THANK GOD FOR...

1. _____
2. _____
3. _____

FOOD INTAKE

ACTIVITIES

JOURNAL ENTRY

☐ **MORNING SKINCARE**

☐ _____

☐ _____

☐ **EVENING SKINCARE**

DATE _____ M T W T F S S

HOURS SLEPT	ENERGY

VERSE OF THE DAY | MARK 7:15

MOOD

☹ ☹ 😐 🙂 😄

TODAY'S GOALS: _____

_____

I PRAY FOR

BLACK WOMEN ARE

I THANK GOD FOR...

1. _____
2. _____
3. _____

FOOD INTAKE

ACTIVITIES

JOURNAL ENTRY

☐ **MORNING SKINCARE**

☐ _____

☐ _____

☐ **EVENING SKINCARE**

DATE _____ M T W T F S S

HOURS SLEPT	ENERGY

MOOD

😠 🙁 😐 🙂 😄

TODAY'S GOALS: _____
_____

BLACK WOMEN ARE

I THANK GOD FOR...

1. _____
2. _____
3. _____

VERSE OF THE DAY | PROVERBS 25:17

_____
_____
_____
_____

I PRAY FOR

FOOD INTAKE

ACTIVITIES

☐ MORNING SKINCARE

☐ _____

☐ _____

☐ EVENING SKINCARE

JOURNAL ENTRY

_____
_____
_____
_____
_____
_____
_____
_____
_____
_____
_____

DATE _____ M T W T F S S

HOURS SLEPT	ENERGY

VERSE OF THE DAY	EZRA 7:10

_____
_____
_____
_____

MOOD

TODAY'S GOALS: _____

_____

I PRAY FOR
_____
_____

BLACK WOMEN ARE

FOOD INTAKE

I THANK GOD FOR...

1. _____
2. _____
3. _____

ACTIVITIES

☐ **MORNING SKINCARE**

☐ _____

☐ _____

☐ **EVENING SKINCARE**

JOURNAL ENTRY

_____
_____
_____
_____
_____
_____
_____
_____
_____
_____
_____
_____
_____

DATE _____ M T W T F S S

HOURS SLEPT	ENERGY

VERSE OF THE DAY | **MATTHEW 7:7**

_____

_____

_____

_____

MOOD

TODAY'S GOALS: _____

_____

I PRAY FOR

BLACK WOMEN ARE

FOOD INTAKE

I THANK GOD FOR...

1. _____
2. _____
3. _____

ACTIVITIES

JOURNAL ENTRY

☐ **MORNING SKINCARE**

☐ _____

☐ _____

☐ **EVENING SKINCARE**

DATE _____ M T W T F S S

HOURS SLEPT	ENERGY

VERSE OF THE DAY | **1 KINGS 8:56**

MOOD

I PRAY FOR

TODAY'S GOALS: _____

_____

BLACK WOMEN ARE

FOOD INTAKE

I THANK GOD FOR...

1. _____
2. _____
3. _____

ACTIVITIES

JOURNAL ENTRY

☐ **MORNING SKINCARE**

☐ _____

☐ _____

☐ **EVENING SKINCARE**

DATE _____ M T W T F S S

HOURS SLEPT	ENERGY

MOOD

TODAY'S GOALS: _____

_____

BLACK WOMEN ARE

I THANK GOD FOR...

1. _____
2. _____
3. _____

I PRAY FOR

FOOD INTAKE

ACTIVITIES

JOURNAL ENTRY

☐ MORNING SKINCARE

☐ _____

☐ _____

☐ EVENING SKINCARE

DATE _____ M T W T F S S

HOURS SLEPT	ENERGY

MOOD

😠 ☹️ 😐 🙂 😄

VERSE OF THE DAY	PROVERBS 27:1-2

_____
_____
_____
_____

TODAY'S GOALS: _____
_____

I PRAY FOR
_____
_____

BLACK WOMEN ARE

I THANK GOD FOR...

1. _____
2. _____
3. _____

FOOD INTAKE

ACTIVITIES

JOURNAL ENTRY

☐ **MORNING SKINCARE**

☐ _____

☐ _____

☐ **EVENING SKINCARE**

DATE _____ M T W T F S S

HOURS SLEPT	ENERGY

VERSE OF THE DAY	2 CORINTHI. 4:16

_____
_____
_____
_____

MOOD

😠 ☹️ 😐 🙂 😄

TODAY'S GOALS: _____
_____

I PRAY FOR

_____

BLACK WOMEN ARE

FOOD INTAKE

I THANK GOD FOR...

1. _____
2. _____
3. _____

ACTIVITIES

☐ **MORNING SKINCARE**

☐ _____

☐ _____

☐ **EVENING SKINCARE**

JOURNAL ENTRY

_____
_____
_____
_____
_____
_____
_____
_____
_____
_____
_____
_____
_____
_____

DATE _____ M T W T F S S

HOURS SLEPT	ENERGY

MOOD

VERSE OF THE DAY | PSALMS 1:1

_____
_____
_____
_____

TODAY'S GOALS: _____
_____

I PRAY FOR
_____
_____

BLACK WOMEN ARE

FOOD INTAKE

I THANK GOD FOR...

1. _____
2. _____
3. _____

ACTIVITIES

☐ **MORNING SKINCARE**

☐ _____

☐ _____

☐ **EVENING SKINCARE**

JOURNAL ENTRY

_____
_____
_____
_____
_____
_____
_____
_____
_____
_____
_____
_____
_____

DATE _____ M T W T F S S

HOURS SLEPT	ENERGY

MOOD

☹ 🙁 😐 🙂 😄

VERSE OF THE DAY | **PROVERBS 3:5**

_____
_____
_____
_____

TODAY'S GOALS: _____

_____

I PRAY FOR
_____
_____

BLACK WOMEN ARE
_____

FOOD INTAKE
_____
_____
_____
_____
_____
_____
_____

I THANK GOD FOR...

1. _____
2. _____
3. _____

ACTIVITIES

JOURNAL ENTRY

_____
_____
_____
_____
_____
_____
_____

☐ **MORNING SKINCARE**

☐ _____

☐ _____

☐ **EVENING SKINCARE**

DATE _____ M T W T F S S

HOURS SLEPT	ENERGY

VERSE OF THE DAY	ESTHER 4:13

MOOD

TODAY'S GOALS: _____

_____

I PRAY FOR

BLACK WOMEN ARE

FOOD INTAKE

I THANK GOD FOR...

1. _____
2. _____
3. _____

ACTIVITIES

JOURNAL ENTRY

☐ **MORNING SKINCARE**

☐ _____

☐ _____

☐ **EVENING SKINCARE**

DATE _____ M T W T F S S

HOURS SLEPT	ENERGY

MOOD

😠 😦 😐 🙂 😁

TODAY'S GOALS: _____

_____

BLACK WOMEN ARE

I THANK GOD FOR...

1. _____
2. _____
3. _____

VERSE OF THE DAY | **1 JOHN 1:9**

_____
_____
_____
_____

I PRAY FOR

FOOD INTAKE

ACTIVITIES

☐ **MORNING SKINCARE**

☐ _____

☐ _____

☐ **EVENING SKINCARE**

JOURNAL ENTRY

DATE _____ M T W T F S S

HOURS SLEPT	ENERGY

MOOD

😠 ☹️ 😐 🙂 😄

VERSE OF THE DAY | **EXODUS 15:11**

TODAY'S GOALS: _____

_____

I PRAY FOR

BLACK WOMEN ARE

FOOD INTAKE

I THANK GOD FOR...

1. _____
2. _____
3. _____

ACTIVITIES

JOURNAL ENTRY

☐ **MORNING SKINCARE**

☐ _____

☐ _____

☐ **EVENING SKINCARE**

DATE _____ M T W T F S S

HOURS SLEPT	ENERGY

MOOD

☹ ☹ 😐 🙂 😄

VERSE OF THE DAY | **2 CHRONI. 15:7**

_____
_____
_____
_____

TODAY'S GOALS: _____

_____

I PRAY FOR
_____
_____

BLACK WOMEN ARE
_____

I THANK GOD FOR...

1. _____
2. _____
3. _____

FOOD INTAKE

ACTIVITIES

JOURNAL ENTRY

☐ **MORNING SKINCARE**

☐ _____

☐ _____

☐ **EVENING SKINCARE**

DATE _____ M T W T F S S

HOURS SLEPT	ENERGY

MOOD

VERSE OF THE DAY	JOSHUA 1:8

TODAY'S GOALS: _____

_____

I PRAY FOR

BLACK WOMEN ARE

FOOD INTAKE

I THANK GOD FOR...

1. _____

2. _____

3. _____

ACTIVITIES

JOURNAL ENTRY

☐ **MORNING SKINCARE**

☐ _____

☐ _____

☐ **EVENING SKINCARE**

DATE _____ M T W T F S S

HOURS SLEPT	ENERGY

VERSE OF THE DAY | **HOSEA 10:12**

_____
_____
_____
_____
_____

MOOD

😠 😞 😐 🙂 😄

TODAY'S GOALS: _____

_____

I PRAY FOR
_____
_____

BLACK WOMEN ARE
_____

FOOD INTAKE
_____
_____
_____
_____
_____
_____
_____

I THANK GOD FOR...

1. _____
2. _____
3. _____

ACTIVITIES

☐ **MORNING SKINCARE**

☐ _____

☐ _____

☐ **EVENING SKINCARE**

JOURNAL ENTRY

_____
_____
_____
_____
_____
_____
_____
_____
_____
_____
_____
_____
_____

DATE _____ M T W T F S S

HOURS SLEPT	ENERGY

MOOD

VERSE OF THE DAY | EPHESIANS 2:8-9

_____
_____
_____
_____

TODAY'S GOALS: _____
_____

I PRAY FOR

BLACK WOMEN ARE

I THANK GOD FOR...

1. _____
2. _____
3. _____

FOOD INTAKE

ACTIVITIES

☐ **MORNING SKINCARE**

☐ _____

☐ _____

☐ **EVENING SKINCARE**

JOURNAL ENTRY

_____
_____
_____
_____
_____
_____
_____
_____
_____
_____
_____
_____
_____

DATE _____ M T W T F S S

HOURS SLEPT	ENERGY

VERSE OF THE DAY | **JOB 19:25**

_____
_____
_____
_____

MOOD

😠 😟 😐 🙂 😁

I PRAY FOR

TODAY'S GOALS: _____

_____

BLACK WOMEN ARE

FOOD INTAKE

I THANK GOD FOR...

1. _____
2. _____
3. _____

ACTIVITIES

JOURNAL ENTRY

☐ **MORNING SKINCARE**

☐ _____

☐ _____

☐ **EVENING SKINCARE**

DATE _____ **M T W T F S S**

HOURS SLEPT	ENERGY

VERSE OF THE DAY	JAMES 1:2-3

MOOD

☹ 🙁 😐 🙂 😄

TODAY'S GOALS: _____

_____

I PRAY FOR

BLACK WOMEN ARE

FOOD INTAKE

I THANK GOD FOR...

1. _____
2. _____
3. _____

ACTIVITIES

JOURNAL ENTRY

☐ **MORNING SKINCARE**

☐ _____

☐ _____

☐ **EVENING SKINCARE**

DATE _____ M T W T F S S

HOURS SLEPT	ENERGY

MOOD

😠 ☹️ 😐 🙂 😄

VERSE OF THE DAY | **PROVERBS 17:17**

_____
_____
_____
_____

TODAY'S GOALS: _____

_____

I PRAY FOR
_____
_____

BLACK WOMEN ARE
_____

FOOD INTAKE

I THANK GOD FOR...

1. _____
2. _____
3. _____

ACTIVITIES

JOURNAL ENTRY

_____
_____
_____
_____
_____
_____
_____

☐ **MORNING SKINCARE**

☐ _____

☐ _____

☐ **EVENING SKINCARE**

DATE _____ M T W T F S S

HOURS SLEPT	ENERGY

VERSE OF THE DAY	2 TIMOTHY 1:7

MOOD

TODAY'S GOALS: _____
_____

I PRAY FOR

BLACK WOMEN ARE

FOOD INTAKE

I THANK GOD FOR...

1. _____
2. _____
3. _____

ACTIVITIES

JOURNAL ENTRY

☐ MORNING SKINCARE

☐ _____

☐ _____

☐ EVENING SKINCARE

DATE _____ M T W T F S S

HOURS SLEPT	ENERGY

VERSE OF THE DAY | **PSALMS 30:2**

_____
_____
_____
_____

MOOD

☹ ☹ 😐 🙂 😄

TODAY'S GOALS: _____

_____

I PRAY FOR

BLACK WOMEN ARE

FOOD INTAKE

I THANK GOD FOR...

1. _____
2. _____
3. _____

ACTIVITIES

JOURNAL ENTRY

_____
_____
_____
_____
_____
_____
_____

☐ **MORNING SKINCARE**

☐ _____

☐ _____

☐ **EVENING SKINCARE**

DATE _____ **M T W T F S S**

HOURS SLEPT	ENERGY

MOOD

VERSE OF THE DAY | PROVERBS 1:7

TODAY'S GOALS: _____
_____

I PRAY FOR

BLACK WOMEN ARE

FOOD INTAKE

I THANK GOD FOR...

1. _____
2. _____
3. _____

ACTIVITIES

JOURNAL ENTRY

☐ **MORNING SKINCARE**

☐ _____

☐ _____

☐ **EVENING SKINCARE**

DATE _____ M T W T F S S

HOURS SLEPT	ENERGY

MOOD

😠 😞 😐 🙂 😁

VERSE OF THE DAY **EXODUS 23:24**

_____
_____
_____
_____

TODAY'S GOALS: _____

_____

I PRAY FOR
_____
_____

BLACK WOMEN ARE
_____

FOOD INTAKE

I THANK GOD FOR...

1. _____
2. _____
3. _____

ACTIVITIES

JOURNAL ENTRY

☐ MORNING SKINCARE

☐ _____

☐ _____

☐ EVENING SKINCARE

DATE _____ M T W T F S S

HOURS SLEPT	ENERGY

MOOD

😠 ☹️ 😐 🙂 😄

VERSE OF THE DAY | **PROVERBS 11:2**

TODAY'S GOALS: _____

_____

I PRAY FOR

BLACK WOMEN ARE

FOOD INTAKE

I THANK GOD FOR...

1. _____

2. _____

3. _____

ACTIVITIES

☐ **MORNING SKINCARE**

☐ _____

☐ _____

☐ **EVENING SKINCARE**

JOURNAL ENTRY

DATE _____ M T W T F S S

HOURS SLEPT	ENERGY

VERSE OF THE DAY	1 TIMOTHY 6:10

_____
_____
_____
_____

MOOD

I PRAY FOR
_____
_____

TODAY'S GOALS: _____
_____

FOOD INTAKE

BLACK WOMEN ARE

I THANK GOD FOR...

1. _____
2. _____
3. _____

ACTIVITIES

JOURNAL ENTRY

_____
_____
_____
_____
_____

☐ **MORNING SKINCARE**

☐ _____

☐ _____

☐ **EVENING SKINCARE**

DATE _____ M T W T F S S

HOURS SLEPT	ENERGY

VERSE OF THE DAY	ACTS 20:35

_____
_____
_____
_____

MOOD

😠 🙁 😐 🙂 😄

TODAY'S GOALS: _____
_____

I PRAY FOR
_____
_____

BLACK WOMEN ARE

FOOD INTAKE

I THANK GOD FOR...

1. _____
2. _____
3. _____

ACTIVITIES

JOURNAL ENTRY

☐ **MORNING SKINCARE**

☐ _____

☐ _____

☐ **EVENING SKINCARE**

DATE _____ M T W T F S S

HOURS SLEPT	ENERGY

VERSE OF THE DAY	PROVERBS 17:18

_____
_____
_____
_____

MOOD

TODAY'S GOALS: _____

_____

I PRAY FOR

BLACK WOMEN ARE

FOOD INTAKE

I THANK GOD FOR...

1. _____
2. _____
3. _____

ACTIVITIES

☐ **MORNING SKINCARE**

☐ _____

☐ _____

☐ **EVENING SKINCARE**

JOURNAL ENTRY

_____
_____
_____
_____
_____
_____
_____
_____
_____
_____
_____
_____

DATE _____ M T W T F S S

HOURS SLEPT	ENERGY

VERSE OF THE DAY | **EPHESIANS 5:25**

MOOD

😠 😞 😐 🙂 😄

TODAY'S GOALS: _____

_____

I PRAY FOR

BLACK WOMEN ARE

FOOD INTAKE

I THANK GOD FOR...

1. _____
2. _____
3. _____

ACTIVITIES

JOURNAL ENTRY

☐ **MORNING SKINCARE**

☐ _____

☐ _____

☐ **EVENING SKINCARE**

DATE _____ M T W T F S S

HOURS SLEPT	ENERGY

VERSE OF THE DAY	JOHN 15:1-2

_____
_____
_____
_____

MOOD

☹ ☹ 😐 🙂 😄

I PRAY FOR
_____
_____

TODAY'S GOALS: _____

_____

BLACK WOMEN ARE
_____

FOOD INTAKE

I THANK GOD FOR...

1. _____
2. _____
3. _____

ACTIVITIES

JOURNAL ENTRY

☐ MORNING SKINCARE

☐ _____

☐ _____

☐ EVENING SKINCARE

DATE _____ M T W T F S S

HOURS SLEPT	ENERGY

MOOD

😠 ☹️ 😐 🙂 😄

VERSE OF THE DAY | **REVELATION 1:7**
_____
_____
_____
_____

TODAY'S GOALS: _____
_____

I PRAY FOR
_____
_____

BLACK WOMEN ARE

FOOD INTAKE

I THANK GOD FOR...

1. _____
2. _____
3. _____

ACTIVITIES

☐ **MORNING SKINCARE**

☐ _____

☐ _____

☐ **EVENING SKINCARE**

JOURNAL ENTRY

_____
_____
_____
_____
_____
_____
_____
_____
_____
_____
_____
_____

DATE _____ M T W T F S S

HOURS SLEPT	ENERGY

VERSE OF THE DAY	MATTHEW 17:5

_____
_____
_____
_____

MOOD

I PRAY FOR
_____
_____

TODAY'S GOALS: _____

_____

FOOD INTAKE
_____
_____
_____
_____
_____
_____
_____
_____

BLACK WOMEN ARE
_____

I THANK GOD FOR...

1. _____
2. _____
3. _____

ACTIVITIES

JOURNAL ENTRY

☐ **MORNING SKINCARE**

☐ _____

☐ _____

☐ **EVENING SKINCARE**

DATE _____ M T W T F S S

HOURS SLEPT | ENERGY

MOOD

VERSE OF THE DAY | PSALM 112:5

_____
_____
_____
_____

TODAY'S GOALS: _____
_____

I PRAY FOR

BLACK WOMEN ARE

I THANK GOD FOR...

1. _____
2. _____
3. _____

FOOD INTAKE

ACTIVITIES

☐ **MORNING SKINCARE**

☐ _____

☐ _____

☐ **EVENING SKINCARE**

JOURNAL ENTRY

_____
_____
_____
_____
_____
_____
_____
_____
_____
_____
_____
_____
_____
_____

Please feel free to leave a rating or review
on Amazon. It would be greatly appreciated!

Want more? Check out these books for Christian Black women:

Made in the USA
Monee, IL
16 December 2023